TUNNELS OF TIME

Adapted by Deborah Nash

CW00740432

THE INTERNATIONAL RESCUE TEAM:

SCOTT TRACY

ALAN TRACY

JOHN TRACY

VIRGIL TRACY

GORDON TRACY

PARKER

LADY PENELOPE

Virgil and Gordon were flying Thunderbird 2 through the high mountains of South America. They were on their way to rescue some miners who had been trapped in a landslide.

When they arrived, they removed the rock blocking the entrance of the mine. All the trapped miners escaped safely.

Suddenly, Gordon spotted a huge stone head. He contacted John in Thunderbird 5.

"What do all those symbols mean?" Gordon asked John.

John quickly found out. "They're in a very old language," he said. "It means: This is the Pyramid of the Laughing King. If you dare to disturb my peace, you will join me in my tomb!"

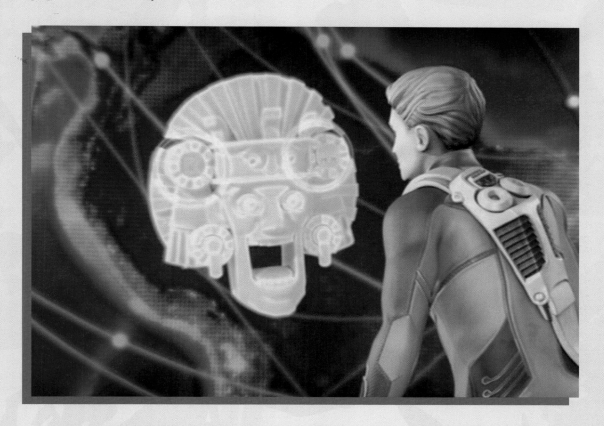

When the rescue work was over, Thunderbird 2 returned to base.

The Pyramid of the Laughing King turned out to be full of ancient treasures!

Professor Harold was the archaeologist in charge of digging up the treasure.

Lady Penelope visited the dig with Parker. She had a special interest in ancient artefacts, and wanted to check that the dig was going well. She had heard rumours that Professor Harold might be up to no good.

Gordon went too. He wanted to help – and he also wanted to find out what was behind the big stone head he had found.

It was dark in the tunnels, and Parker wasn't happy. Just when he thought he had come to a dead end, there was a loud rumble. A secret doorway appeared in the wall!

"This doorway must lead to gold and treasure," said Professor Harold, excitedly.

He hurried down the steps to a little room, and pressed a round stone.

The others were trapped, and the little room was filling up with poisonous gas!

I will get help!" shouted the professor, as he stumbled back to the entrance. "You keep hunting for that gold!"

Inside the little room, Parker sat down on a ledge. "If I'm going to die of poisonous gas, I might as well get comfortable," he said.

At once, a stone shifted and another tunnel appeared.

Gordon, Parker and Lady Penelope walked along the gloomy tunnel. At least it was taking them away from the poisonous gas! Then Parker stepped on a trip wire.

Spears came shooting out of the tunnel walls!
"Help!" shouted Parker, as the spears pinned him
to a wall.

Parker, Lady Penelope and Gordon escaped from the spears, but more surprises were still to come. A gigantic spiked hammer swung down and nearly hit them!

Back at camp, Professor Harold was talking to John. "The others are fine," he lied. "They're just taking a tour. There's no need for you to come here!"

John tried to contact Gordon, but he couldn't. Then he ran a scan on the mountain and he found poisonous gas. He knew Professor Harold was lying.

John told the other members of International Rescue what had happened.

"Team, we must help them!" said Scott.

FIVE, FOUR, THREE, TWO, ONE!
Thunderbirds 1 and 2 are go!

Virgil and Scott quickly reached the mountain where their team was trapped.

Gordon, Lady Penelope and Parker had been walking through the tunnels for a long time. Finally, they reached the centre of the pyramid. A huge golden statue of the Laughing King was looking down at them.

Suddenly, the floor started to crumble away under them! They managed to climb up to the top of the statue.

"We disturbed the Laughing King's peace!" cried Parker. "Now we'll share his tomb!"

"We won't!" shouted Gordon. "Grab that rope!"

The rope came from Thunderbird 2. It made a hole in the mountain and lifted them to safety.

When Gordon, Lady Penelope and Parker were safely on the ground, Professor Harold came rushing over to them. He pretended he was worried about them – but he was worried only about the treasure!

Everyone knew that Professor Harold had lied and put the others in danger. He lost his job as chief archaeologist.

As for the Laughing King, no one would ever disturb his peace again.